WRITING MY LIFE
The Step-by-Step Autobiography

WRITING MY LIFE

The Step-by-Step Autobiography

Alison Bing

BARNES
&NOBLE
B O O K S
NEW YORK

Text design by Lundquist Design, NY

ISBN: 0-7607-3346-5

Printed and bound in the United States

02 03 04 05 06 MC 7 6 5 4 3 2 1

TABLE OF CONTENTS

INTRODUCTION

Your autobiography: It's your story, and you're sticking to it

Obey the impulse

Admit it—you've experienced the autobiographical impulse. You were talking about a funny thing that happened to you the other day, and someone spoke the magic words: "You know, you really should write some of this stuff down…" Or perhaps you took a look at the paper trail you're leaving behind you—receipts, diplomas, job applications, driver's license photos—and realized that that the story it tells about you leaves out a lot of the best parts. Or maybe some kind and eminently wise individual gave you this book, and that got you thinking about all the moments in your life worth remembering.

Now's the time to obey that impulse—and quick, before you come up with still more memorable moments. As the memories pile up, some inevitably get lost in the shuffle. An autobiography helps you organize your thoughts, so that the best ones are always within reach. Just think of it as a filing cabinet for all the mental notes you've made over the years.

Getting started

Once you get started, you'll wonder why you've waited this long to write your autobiography. Could be you've been misled to believe that to be a worthy autobiography subject, first you have to invent the widget that fixes the hole in the ozone layer or paint a masterpiece or produce some other public display of genius. But consider this: Your life is already a unique and valuable invention, and when you connect the dots between the defining moments in your life you've got one amazing picture. Just put it on paper and hey, presto! You're an autobiographer.

Is it really that simple? In a word: Yes. You don't need to block out a summer to do it, or wait until you're retired. Add up the time you usually kill on the bus ride home, in line at the checkout counter, or at the gym, and you'll find there's already room for reflection in your schedule. All you need now is a little courage, and a little prodding. We trust you have the courage part covered; otherwise, you wouldn't be picking up this book in the first place. And as for prodding—well, that's what this book is all about.

Organization of this book

Writing My Life takes you through every stage of your life story, including:

- Beginnings: your early childhood, from your first day on earth through your kindergarten heyday
- Childhood: takes you through elementary school, from spelling bees to long division—and of course recess
- Adolescence: sees you through those awkward preteen years and your high school dramas and traumas
- Coming of Age: when you strike out on your own, land

your first job and live on bagels with ten roommates

• Coming into Your Own: adulthood in full swing, when you're finally building a life and a name for yourself, too

• Self-Realization: when you reach maturity at last, and earn the right to enjoy life like a kid

How to use this book

This book is organized in chronological fashion in six chapters: Beginnings, Childhood, Adolescence, Coming of Age, Coming into Your Own, and Self-Realization. But that doesn't mean you have to write it that way. If you're inspired to launch right into your adolescence, do it. And you can define the age span of each chapter as you please. If you think you came of age at 16 or that your childhood still isn't over, then that's the way you should write those chapters. Try not to shy away from any one chapter, though—sometimes the toughest chapters of your life are the most worth writing.

In each of the six chapters, you'll find three methods you can use to get your memories out of your subconscious, and onto paper where they belong: Q&A, Artifacts, and Interviews. The Q&A method will come naturally to those who are already used to talking about their lives in some detail—if you're chatty or enjoy magazine quizzes or job interviews, this is the method for you. The Artifacts Method is ideal for those who don't have much time for musing in their daily schedule, but find that the memories come flooding back with some sensory input—a particular smell, song, or photo. If you're scientifically-minded, innately inquisitive, or meticulous, the Interviews Method is the natural choice to jog your memory and check to see if those memories serve you correctly before committing them to posterity. Try one method that comes naturally, and one that challenges you—it'll enrich your autobiography, and your experience of writing it too.

You'll notice glancing through these books that there are a whopping lot of specific, leading questions in here—and with any luck, more than a few that jolt your memory into action. These are the types of questions avid interviewers (such as yours truly) ask their subjects: they mine for meaningful memories, they keep you focused on telling details instead of vague generalities and they're occasionally offbeat to keep you thinking. This is not a test, so you never have to worry about giving a wrong answer and you can skip as many questions as you like. But try not to dodge the difficult ones; play a hard-hitting reporter with yourself, and get to the heart of the matter.

An instant classic
Your autobiography is more than just another book. It's a process of self-discovery, an opportunity to acknowledge the important influences and people in your life, and a chance to tell your story as only you can.

So, just add memories, and stir
That's all there is to it. Don't let anyone tell you otherwise. Now get writing that story of yours—it's already been a lifetime in the making.

BEGINNINGS

Think back...

Just ask Darwin: Origins are tricky business. None of us can remember our own beginnings, so we have to rely on artifacts and other people to tell us how we got our start in life. Problem is, the stories we're told about our early childhood are often contradictory—one relative may remember you as a colicky baby, while another may insist you never cried. Your challenge as an autobiographer is to determine which versions of events make the most sense to you, given what else you've heard, and any evidence from that era that supports one particular account.

If you're going for scientific accuracy here, you may be disappointed. We know a lot more about who we are now than who we were back then, so we tend to reduce our infant selves to miniature versions of our grown-up selves. But if you dress up your past to look like your present, you'll make your younger self seem unreal—like a child dolled up as an adult for a beauty pageant. Just try to record your earliest memories in all their childlike wonder as faithfully as you can, without letting your adult self intervene too much and explain them all away.

Television can interfere with your best storytelling intentions, too. TV has us trained to look for that simple plot device, that destined-for-greatness story arc or humble beginnings hook that would add an epic touch to our life story—all while wrapping it up with a big obvious bow in under an hour. True epics are never so simple, of course; it's hard to imagine what the *Odyssey* would've been like if

Homer had chintzed out on the character development and cut straight to the chase. So tell it like you lived it, with all the character-building inconsistencies and imaginative leaps, not as you think other people will expect to hear it—and become the hero of your own epic tale.

Forge ahead!

Where to begin? Anywhere you want—birth, your earliest memory, your first words, that time you ate your birthday candles. Basically, whenever you feel you got your start in life. Write until you think you're starting to delve into your childhood memories; that's a sign you're ready for the next chapter.

Below are three methods to get your memories out of your subconscious, and onto paper where they belong. These are: Q&A, Artifacts, and Interviews. Try one method that comes naturally, and one that challenges you—it'll enrich your autobiography, and your experience of writing it too.

The Q&A Method

Jot down your responses to at least a few of the questions that seem relevant to you under each of the four main topics: Firsts, Family, Make-believe, and Home. Feel free to add others or go off on tangents as the spirit moves you. If you find yourself hesitating, you might try reading the questions aloud and recording your spoken answers with a voice recorder. Then as you play back your recording, write down the interesting parts of your answers and elaborate on them as you see fit. Your answers should bring your origins into focus, and provide a few juicy anecdotes besides.

Q&A Topic #1: Firsts

Memories

What's your earliest memory? Describe. _____

_____

_____

_____

_____

_____

What's the very first family holiday you remember? ____

_____

_____

_____

_____

_____

Who are the first people outside of your family you can remember? Describe. _____

_____

_____

_____

_____

_____

What particularly happy moment do you remember from when you were very young? _____

_____

_____

_____

_____

_____

Favorites

Did you have a security blanket? Describe. When did you give it up, and why? _____

_____

_____

_____

_____

What was your favorite stuffed animal or doll? What did you name it, and why? _____

_____

_____

_____

_____

_____

What songs or stories did you like best when you were very young? Can you remember why? _____

_____

_____

_____

_____

_____

What was your favorite thing to eat as a young child? Did you get to have it often? _____

_____

_____

_____

_____

_____

Words

What were your first words? Who taught them to you? What language were they? Were you very talkative as a baby and as a toddler? _____

_____

_____

_____

_____

Did you ever say something as a baby that older family members can still recall? What? Why do you think they remember this particular comment so vividly? _____

_____

_____

_____

_____

Creative expression

Did you make a lot of drawings when you were little? What did your earliest drawings look like? _____

_____

_____

_____

_____

What music appealed to you the most back then? Did you dance to music when you were very little? What did you look like when you danced? _____

_____

_____

_____

Parents

Who primarily raised you? What are their names and relationship to you? _____

_____

_____

_____

_____

_____

What is your full given name, according to your birth certificate? Do you know the story of how you were named? Describe. _____

_____

_____

_____

_____

If you have any very early memories of your birth parents, what are they? _____

_____

_____

_____

_____

Were you legally adopted? By whom? What did your adoptive parent(s) tell you about your adoption? _____

_____

_____

_____

_____

Do you know the story of how your birth parents, adoptive parents, or parent and stepparent met? Describe. _____

_____

_____

_____

_____

_____

_____

Where were your parents born? _____

_____

_____

_____

_____

_____

_____

What were their occupations and main interests when you came into their lives? _____

_____

_____

_____

_____

_____

What is your fondest memory of them when you were little?

_____

_____

_____

_____

_____

Siblings

Do you have any siblings? How much older or younger than you are they? What are their names? _____

_____

_____

_____

_____

_____

When you were very little, did you have one particular sibling that you liked best? Who? Why? _____

_____

_____

_____

_____

_____

Did you fight much with your sibling(s) when you were very young? About what? _____

_____

_____

_____

_____

_____

Can you remember what you called your sibling(s) when you were little? What did they call you? _____

_____

_____

_____

_____

Grandparents

Did you know your grandparents when you were little? What do you know about where they were born and how they were raised? _____

_____
_____
_____
_____
_____

How involved were your grandparents in raising you? Why?

_____
_____
_____
_____
_____
_____

What are your earliest memories of your grandparents? __

_____
_____
_____
_____
_____

Where did they live when you were little? Did you visit them often? What do you remember most about visiting your grandparents? _____

_____
_____
_____

Can you recall something about your grandparents' home that particularly fascinated you? _____

_____

_____

_____

_____

What's your favorite story that your grandparent(s) told you? _____

_____

_____

_____

_____

_____

_____

_____

_____

_____

_____

_____

_____

_____

_____

_____

_____

_____

_____

_____

_____

_____

Relatives

Did you see any of your aunts, uncles, and cousins often when you were little? Which ones? _____

_____

_____

_____

_____

_____

Did you have any favorites? Who? Why? _____

_____

_____

_____

_____

_____

Did you have any relatives you dreaded seeing? Who? Why?

_____

_____

_____

_____

_____

_____

Is there anyone you refer to as an aunt, uncle, or cousin who isn't actually related to you, but has always been like family to you? Describe. _____

_____

_____

_____

_____

Q&A Topic #3: Make-believe

Games

What were your favorite games when you were very young?
Why? _____

_____

_____

_____

_____

_____

Can you recall any games you made up with your siblings or
neighbors? Describe. _____

_____

_____

_____

_____

_____

How competitive were you? Would you cheat or change the
rules to win? _____

_____

_____

_____

_____

_____

Did you ever play dress-up? What did you like to dress up
as most of all? _____

_____

_____

_____

_____

Magic

Can you remember having an invisible or imaginary friend?
Describe. _____

_____

_____

_____

_____

Were you very superstitious when you were little? How did
you ward off bad luck or evil spirits? _____

_____

_____

_____

_____

Ever pretend you had magic powers? What kind? _____

_____

_____

_____

Did you ever imagine there were monsters under your bed,
or in your closet? How did you make them go away? _____

_____

_____

_____

Can you recall believing in fairies, witches, angels, or other
magical beings? Why do you think you believed in them?

_____

_____

_____

_____

Stories

What stories did you beg your parent(s) to read to you over and over? What was it you liked so much about those particular books? _____

_____
_____
_____
_____
_____

What story scared the tar out of you? Why? _____

_____
_____
_____
_____
_____

Did anyone make up bedtime stories just for you? Who? What were those stories about? _____

_____
_____
_____
_____
_____

Who do you remember as the best storyteller in your family? Why? _____

_____
_____
_____
_____

Dreams

Did you have nightmares often? What were they usually about? Why do you think you were so preoccupied with that subject as a small child? _____

_____

_____

_____

_____

_____

_____

_____

_____

Is there one particular dream or nightmare that stands out in your memory? Describe. _____

_____

_____

_____

_____

_____

_____

Was this dream or nightmare based on fact, or did it ever come true? Explain. _____

_____

_____

_____

_____

_____

Q&A Topic #4: Home
Your early childhood home

Did you move around a lot as a young kid, or did you spend
your early years in one particular place? _____

_____

_____

_____

_____

What are the five words that spring to mind when you
think of the first home you remember clearly? Why? ____

_____

_____

_____

_____

What smells come to mind when you think of that childhood home? Why? What sounds do you associate with that
home? _____

_____

_____

_____

_____

Was there some cabinet, shelf, closet, or room to which you
were denied access? Describe. Did you ever get in there
anyway? What happened? _____

_____

_____

_____

_____

Room

Did you share your room with anyone when you were little? Who? How did you like that? _____

_____

_____

_____

_____

_____

What was on the walls of your room? Did you have wallpaper? What was the pattern on it? _____

_____

_____

_____

_____

_____

When you were very young, if you had to rescue one item from a fire, what one thing in your room would you have rescued? _____

_____

_____

_____

_____

How tidy or untidy was your room, usually? Describe what you might find on the floor of your room on a typical day.

_____

_____

_____

_____

Stomping grounds

What was your favorite place to play outside? Why? What playground or park scene can you remember most vividly?

_____

_____

_____

_____

_____

Did you go to a daycare center or nursery school? What do you remember about the place? The other kids? The daycare provider? _____

_____

_____

_____

_____

_____

Did you play at a neighbor's house often? What do you remember about it? _____

_____

_____

_____

_____

Did you have some neighbors you particularly liked? Any you particularly disliked? Why? _____

_____

_____

_____

_____

The Artifacts Method

To bring your memories to the surface, try digging up a few souvenirs of your early years. Pick at least three items from the lists below to examine, and use the accompanying questions as a guide to further discoveries. If you pay close attention to these objects, you'll find they have a lot to say about the young child you once were—and the person you now are.

Birth certificates, announcements, and cards:

Where and when exactly where you born? _____

_____

_____

_____

Were you born prematurely, or were there any complications with your birth? _____

_____

_____

_____

Lock of baby hair or first tooth:

Were you born with hair? What color was your hair? Did your hair look like your mother's or father's? _____

_____

_____

_____

Can you remember when you lost your first tooth? Did you leave it for the Tooth Fairy? What did you get in return?

_____

_____

_____

Baby clothes and shoes:

How were you usually dressed as a baby? _____

_____

_____

_____

_____

Were they hand-me-downs? Whose? _____

_____

_____

_____

Why do you think your parent(s) saved these particular items you wore? _____

_____

_____

_____

Drawings:

What characters appear most often in your earliest drawings? _____

_____

_____

_____

Did you ever draw a picture of your childhood home, relative, or pet? Does this drawing remind you of anything about your early home life that you'd forgotten? _____

_____

_____

_____

Family photos:

Where were most of the photos of you as a young child taken? Do you have any pictures of family vacations when you were little? _____

_____

_____

_____

_____

_____

Do you have any photos taken inside your home or a relative's home? What can you remember about the furniture or knick-knacks shown in the background? _____

_____

_____

_____

_____

Who appears with you most often in photos taken when you were little? Why? _____

_____

_____

_____

_____

Who in the photo can you remember only vaguely? What is it that you do remember about these people? _____

_____

_____

_____

_____

Toys:

Are there pictures of you holding a toy? Is it the same toy? What do you remember about this toy? _____

_____

_____

_____

_____

Do you remember what you called your favorite toy, and why? _____

_____

_____

_____

Where can you recall taking this toy with you? _____

_____

_____

_____

Were you willing to share this toy with your sibling(s)? Why or why not? _____

_____

_____

_____

Children's albums, songbook, etc.

Can you remember any songs you particularly liked when you were very young, and why? _____

_____

_____

_____

Which songs or lullabies always got you to quiet down? ___

_____

_____

_____

_____

_____

Family recipes or comfort food dishes:

What foods do you most associate with early childhood, and why? _____

_____

_____

_____

_____

_____

Did your parent(s) make you any special foods when you were sick? Describe. _____

_____

_____

_____

Other:

Describe. _____

_____

_____

_____

_____

_____

_____

_____

_____

The Interviews Method

If you've hit upon a topic you'd like to explore further or aren't sure your memory serves you correctly, you might want to interview people who knew you early on in life. Choose interview candidates from The Usual Suspects list below, or identify a few candidates of your own. Their accounts can help broaden your perspective and ground your story in fact. Be sure to ask your interview subjects in advance if they can spare an hour for the interview—that way they won't get testy halfway through, and you'll get much better material. The Sample Interview Questions included below should get your interview rolling.

The Usual Suspects

Parents, foster or adoptive parents, and stepparents
Grandparents
Godparents
Relatives
Neighbors
Early childhood playmates
Daycare providers
Nursery school teachers
Pediatrician
Librarians, shopkeepers, and others in your hometown who knew you back then
Others: _____

Sample Interview Questions

Here are six interview questions to get you started—feel free to supplement or replace these questions with your own. You may want to record the interview on a voice recorder, and jot down the most interesting quotes here later on. Keep in mind that a single question can take 5-10 minutes to answer, depending on how chatty your interviewee is and whether you ask follow-up questions.

I remember that you were there when I _____ as a very young child. What do you remember about that time? _____

_____

_____

_____

How would you describe me as a baby? What about as a toddler? _____

_____

_____

_____

What activities did I seem most interested in when I was very young? _____

_____

_____

_____

Can you tell me what people, places, and toys seemed to be my favorites in my preschool days? _____

_____

_____

_____

_____

_____

_____

Was there a particular story I always wanted to hear, song I always sang, or game I always wanted to play when I was very young? _____

_____

_____

_____

How did I seem similar to other children you knew, and how did I seem different? _____

_____

_____

_____

_____

_____

_____

_____

_____

_____

_____

_____

_____

_____

_____

_____

_____

_____

_____

CHILDHOOD

Think back…

Childhood memories are a lot like ice cream: they melt away faster than you think, and they can leave you feeling queasy if you try to digest them too quickly. They are notoriously hard to capture on paper, and absorbing them takes time. Casual storytellers often neglect the nuances of childhood, and describe it as just one of two flavors: idyllic or traumatic. As a soon-to-be accomplished autobiographer, you can do better—try to figure out where that lingering emotional aftertaste comes from. Was it your first tantalizing taste of discovery at a science fair, or the bitterness of a playground scuffle? Did these two events happen on the same day, so that you've come to associate the sweet with the sour?

Your childhood associations may seem nonsensical to you now, but elementary school kids make intuitive and imaginative leaps that adults don't—our imaginations aren't always as flexible as they used to be. Limber up and follow your childhood line of logic, and it may lead you to unforeseen self-discoveries. If memories of your childhood remain elusive despite your most acrobatic attempts at recollection, don't be too hard on yourself. There's only so much room at the forefront of your mind, and long-ago playground dramas don't always make it right up there with where you parked the car.

The good news is, you don't have to remember entire episodes from your childhood to write a compelling autobiography—just a few specific, telling details. Think of Marcel Proust; the man recalled a single memorable madeleine he ate as a boy, and *voilà!* Hundreds of pages of eloquent prose flowed from his pen, which turned into the classic *Remembrance of Things Past*. Try pinpointing just one deep impression that has stayed with you ever since your childhood, then tracing it to a formative experience—and let your pen reveal your own timeless truths.

Forge ahead!

Where to begin? Anywhere you want—first grade, losing your first tooth, strutting around the neighborhood in your superhero costume. Basically, whenever you feel your childhood really got going. Write until you think you're starting to delve into your adolescent memories; that's a sign you're ready for the next chapter.

Below are three methods to get your memories out of your subconscious, and onto paper where they belong. These are Q&A, Artifacts, and Interviews. Try one method that comes naturally, and one that challenges you—it'll enrich your autobiography, and your experience of writing it too.

The Q&A Method

Jot down your responses to at least a few of the questions that seem relevant to you under each of the four main topics: Friends, School, Pursuits, and Occasions. Feel free to add others or go off on tangents as the spirit moves you. If you find yourself hesitating, you might try reading the questions aloud and recording your spoken answers with a voice recorder. Then as you play back your recording, write down the interesting parts of your answers and elaborate on them as you see fit. Your answers should bring your childhood into focus, and provide a few juicy anecdotes besides.

Q&A Topic #1: Friends
Neighborhood

Who did you play with most often in your grade school days? Why? _____

_____

_____

_____

_____

Did you form any clubs with your friends? What was the mission of the club? What was your role in it? Who did you exclude? Why? _____

_____

_____

_____

_____

Where did you usually play in your neighborhood? Describe. What made this place a fun place for you? ____

_____

_____

_____

_____

Did your friends ever entrust you with any secrets? What were they? Did you keep them, or tell someone? What happened? _____

_____

_____

_____

_____

Did any of your neighbors have lenient rules, junk food, pets or fancy toys you wished you could have? Describe. How big a factor was this in your friendship with them? _____

_____

_____

_____

_____

Did you find out anything about your adult neighbors from their kids that they wouldn't have wanted you to know? Did you tell anyone about it? What happened? _____

_____

_____

_____

_____

Did you have any neighbors you particularly looked up to? Why? _____

_____

_____

_____

_____

_____

_____

_____

_____

_____

_____

_____

_____

Family friends

What family friends can you recall visiting on vacations? Did you ever take road trips with them? Describe. _____

_____

_____

_____

_____

_____

Are there certain kids your parents made you play with, even though you didn't really like them? Describe. _____

_____

_____

_____

_____

_____

Can you remember any friends of your parent(s) or sibling(s) who were a permanent fixture in your house, or were invited along on family vacations? Describe. _____

_____

_____

_____

_____

Who is the first adult you can remember thinking of as a friend? How did you get to be friends? _____

_____

_____

_____

_____

Teammates

Were you ever the first or the last to be chosen for a team during your grade school days? Why? How did that feel?

_____

_____

_____

_____

Which intramural or official school sports teams did you join, and why? Who were your friends on these teams? __

_____

_____

_____

_____

What positions did you play on these teams? Why? What positions did you want to play? Did you ever get to be team captain? How? _____

_____

_____

_____

_____

Can you remember a time when you felt the outcome of a game was all up to you? Describe. How did your teammates treat you afterward? _____

_____

_____

_____

_____

_____

"Little friends"

Can you remember referring to someone as your boyfriend or girlfriend in elementary school? Who was that person? What was your relationship like? How did it start, and end?

_____

_____

_____

_____

_____

Is there anyone you had a crush on in elementary school? Who was it? Did you ever express your feelings? How? What was the response? _____

_____

_____

_____

_____

Do you remember playing doctor with another kid? Who? Where? Were you found out? _____

_____

_____

_____

_____

Was there someone you were always teased about liking? Did you really like that person? How did you respond to the teasing? _____

_____

_____

_____

Classmates

Who did you always try to sit next to in class? Did the teacher ever have to separate you two? Why? _____

_____

_____

_____

_____

_____

Who did you dread sitting near in class? Why? _____

_____

_____

_____

_____

_____

Which of your classmates did you usually play with at recess? Why? What games did you usually play together?

_____

_____

_____

_____

Did you ever lie about how well you did on a test or homework assignment so that you would be accepted by your classmates? Describe. _____

_____

_____

_____

_____

Were you ever the class clown? Which of your antics did your classmates find particularly funny? Did it get you into trouble? Why did you try to make people laugh? _____

_____

_____

_____

_____

Who was the class tattletale? Did that person ever get you in trouble? Did you ever take revenge? Did you ever tell on a classmate? Why? How did that feel? _____

_____

_____

_____

_____

Did you hang out with a classmate that got you into trouble, or was considered a bad influence on you? Why? Was this kid really so bad? _____

_____

_____

_____

_____

Can you remember shunning or shutting out any of your classmates for a period of time? Why? Was that person ever accepted back into the fold? Why? _____

_____

_____

_____

_____

Teachers

Who was your favorite teacher in elementary school? Why?

_____
_____
_____
_____

What about your least favorite teacher? Why? What teacher were you most afraid of? Why? _____

_____
_____
_____

Were you ever considered the teacher's pet by your classmates? Why? Were you? _____

_____
_____
_____

Did you ever have a crush on a teacher in elementary school? Which one? Why? _____

_____
_____
_____

Did your teacher ever send you to the principal's office, or call your parents in for a parent-teacher conference? Why? What was the outcome? _____

_____
_____
_____

Subjects

What was your favorite subject in elementary school? Did this change over time? Explain. _____

_____

_____

_____

What was your least favorite subject? Why? Did your attitude toward this subject ever change? How? _____

_____

_____

_____

What did your report card usually look like? What incentives or punishments did your parents impose to improve or maintain your performance? _____

_____

_____

_____

Was there a subject in which your parents or teachers expected you to excel? What one? Why? How did you respond to the pressure? _____

_____

_____

_____

Did you ever fail any subjects? Which ones? Why? Did you get in trouble? How? _____

_____

_____

Assignments

What class project or assignment was your favorite in elementary school? Why? How much time did you spend on it? _____

_____
_____
_____
_____

Did you ever work on a group project with other classmates? What do you remember about the experience? Who ended up doing the bulk of the work? Why? _____

_____
_____
_____
_____

Did your teachers ever pair you with a kid that you didn't particularly like on a project? How did you deal with it? Did it change your attitude toward that kid? _____

_____
_____
_____
_____

Did a project you worked on ever receive special recognition? Describe. _____

_____
_____
_____
_____

Q&A Topic #3: Pursuits

Collections

Did you collect anything in particular when you were a kid? What was it? What got you so interested in it? _____

_____

_____

_____

_____

_____

Who did you know that shared your passion for collecting, or traded with you? _____

_____

_____

_____

_____

Did you ever go to swap meets or special shops in your pursuit of more items for you collection? Describe. What did you find there? _____

_____

_____

_____

_____

What were some of the prize specimens in your collection? Why? _____

_____

_____

_____

_____

Music

Did you ever sing in a concert or choir performance? What vocal range were you assigned? What songs did you sing? Where? How big was the audience? _____

_____

_____

_____

_____

Did you have a solo? Did you have to audition for it? How did it go? _____

_____

_____

_____

_____

Can you recall playing in an orchestra or band performance or recital? What instrument? What pieces of music did you play? Where? How many people were there? Were you nervous? _____

_____

_____

_____

_____

Did you ever have a solo, or play in first chair position? How were you selected? How did you do at the actual performance? _____

_____

_____

_____

Performances

Were you ever in a school play, dance performance, or local theater production? What role did you play? How were you selected for it? _____

_____

_____

_____

_____

_____

Did you wear a costume? What did it look like? Who picked it out or made it? How did you feel wearing it? __

_____

_____

_____

_____

_____

Did you have any lines? What were they? Did you ever forget them onstage? Did you ad lib? _____

_____

_____

_____

_____

_____

What was the best part of being in this performance? __

_____

_____

_____

_____

Competitions

Did your school have a field day or school olympics? What events did you compete in? How did you prepare for the big day? How did you do? _____

_____

_____

_____

Did you ever participate in a science fair, or in a spelling bee? How did you do? How did you feel about it? _____

_____

_____

_____

Did you ever enter an art project, story or poem you made into a contest? How did it do? How did you feel about it?

_____

_____

_____

Did a team you were on ever play in a tournament? What do you remember about it? Did you win? _____

_____

_____

_____

Did you have a competitive nature as a kid? Did you ever let someone else win? Do you think anyone ever let you win? Explain. _____

_____

_____

Q&A Topic #4: Occasions

Trips

What family vacations or camping trips do you remember most fondly? Why? What were some of the highlights?

_____

_____

_____

_____

_____

Did you ever have any disasters on a family vacation? Describe. _____

_____

_____

_____

_____

_____

What tourist attraction made the biggest impression on you as a kid? Why? _____

_____

_____

_____

_____

What games did you play in the car on family road trips? Did you ever sing songs? Which ones? _____

_____

_____

_____

_____

Holidays

What relatives did you usually spend the holidays with? How were you expected to behave around them? Did you?

_____

_____

_____

_____

What family holiday traditions were your favorites as a kid? Why? _____

_____

_____

_____

_____

Is there one holiday that stands out in your mind as especially enjoyable or meaningful? Why? _____

_____

_____

_____

What's the best present you remember getting as a kid? What made it so great? _____

_____

_____

_____

What foods did you only get on holidays? Who made them? Did you help? _____

_____

_____

_____

Moves

Were you ever the new kid in school? What was that first day like for you? Who was the first person to befriend you?

_____

_____

_____

_____

Did you change schools a lot as a kid? Why? How did you feel about it? Were there certain moves that were particularly smooth or rocky for you? _____

_____

_____

_____

_____

Did you keep in touch with people from your old neighborhood once you'd moved out? Who? _____

_____

_____

_____

_____

Did you ever move to a new country as a kid? Was it hard for you to adjust to a different culture? How quickly did you pick up the local language? What do you remember liking best and least about your new home? _____

_____

_____

_____

_____

Summer camp

What was the name of your camp? Where was it? Did it serve any particular educational or religious purpose? _____

_____

_____

_____

How old were you the first time you went to camp? Did you go often? _____

_____

_____

_____

_____

What summer activities did you like best? What did you enjoy the least? Why? Do you remember any especially thrilling or scary adventures you had at camp? _____

_____

_____

_____

_____

What fellow campers do you remember best? Why? _____

_____

_____

_____

Who were your favorite and least favorite counselors? Why?

_____

_____

_____

The Artifacts Method

To bring your memories to the surface, try digging up a few souvenirs of your childhood. Try to pick at least three items from the lists below to examine, and use the accompanying questions as a guide to further discoveries. If you pay close attention to these objects, you'll find they have a lot to say about the child you once were—and the person you now are.

Notes passed in class, Valentines, and birthday cards:
Do you remember getting in trouble for passing this note? Explain. Did you write notes in class often? What kinds of things did they usually say? _____

_____

_____

_____

_____

Which Valentines or birthday cards do you particularly treasure? Why? Can you describe your reaction when you first received them? _____

_____

_____

_____

_____

Did you make any of these cards? What do they look like? Why do you think the recipient has kept them for all these years? _____

_____

_____

_____

Collections (trading cards, dolls, comics, rocks, action figures, etc.):

Which items were your favorites? Why? _____

_____

_____

_____

Do you remember how you came by the prize items in your collection? Did someone give them to you? What was the occasion? _____

_____

_____

_____

Can you remember begging your parent(s) for this item? Why? What finally wore your parent(s) down? Did you have to do chores or save your allowance for it? _____

_____

_____

_____

Which items in your collection are the most valuable? Why? _____

_____

_____

Do any of these items show signs of wear and tear? How did they get damaged? How did you feel when it happened?

_____

_____

_____

Team, club, or camp uniforms:

How did you feel when you wore this uniform? Why? Did this change over time? _____

_____

_____

_____

_____

_____

What did you usually do at meetings, practices, or outings?

_____

_____

_____

_____

_____

_____

Do you remember when and why you first joined the club or team? Why did you stay or quit? _____

_____

_____

_____

_____

_____

Did you ever go on any road trips or camp overnight with this group? Describe. _____

_____

_____

_____

_____

School gear (lunchboxes, backpacks, pencil cases, uniforms, notebooks, etc.):

Did all the other kids have the same kind of lunch boxes and school supplies as you did, or were yours different? How did you feel about that? _____

_____

_____

_____

_____

What did your uniform look like? How did you feel about wearing it? _____

_____

_____

_____

_____

What was usually in your backpack or school bag on a typical school day? _____

_____

_____

_____

_____

_____

Did you doodle on your backpack or notebooks? What?

_____

_____

_____

_____

_____

School projects (science fair projects, dioramas, book reports, homework, etc.):

Which of these was a particular favorite project of yours? Why? _____

_____

_____

_____

_____

_____

What project do you remember being especially difficult? Easy? Why? _____

_____

_____

_____

_____

_____

What homework assignments did you dread? Enjoy? Why?

_____

_____

_____

_____

_____

Are there teachers' comments on any of your papers? What do they say? _____

_____

_____

_____

_____

Arts & crafts projects (drawings, homemade holiday decorations, ceramics, etc.):

Which arts and crafts projects at school and camp were your favorites? Why? _____

_____

_____

_____

_____

Can you remember what inspired your choice of style or subject? Describe. _____

_____

_____

_____

_____

Did your classmates, teacher, or camp counselor say anything about your finished art project? What? How did you feel about it? _____

_____

_____

_____

_____

Did you give this art project as a gift? Was it well received? Describe. _____

_____

_____

_____

_____

Programs for school plays, recitals, spelling bees, chess competitions, or concerts:

What part did you play in this event? How did you end up in this role? _____

_____

_____

_____

_____

_____

Did you have stage fright beforehand? How did you deal with it? _____

_____

_____

_____

_____

_____

What do you remember about your performance? _____

_____

_____

_____

_____

_____

What kind of a reception did you receive for your performance? Did you get any compliments, encores, or flowers?

_____

_____

_____

_____

Albums, musical instruments, and sheet music:

What music made the biggest impression on you back then?
Why? _____

_____

_____

_____

_____

_____

Did your parents detest any of your music? What? Were you
allowed to listen to it at home? _____

_____

_____

_____

_____

_____

Do you remember dancing to this music? What were some
of your signature moves? _____

_____

_____

_____

_____

Why did you choose to play this particular musical instrument? Did you take lessons? What do you remember about
them? _____

_____

_____

_____

_____

Ribbons, trophies, plaques, and certificates of recognition:
What activity did you win the most awards doing? Did you
enjoy that activity? Why or why not? _____

_____

_____

_____

_____

_____

What ribbons, trophies, etc. mean the most to you, and
why? _____

_____

_____

_____

_____

_____

Were any of these awards especially hard-won? Which
ones? Describe. _____

_____

_____

_____

_____

_____

Do you remember your main competition for these awards?
How did you handle winning or losing to that person? __

_____

_____

_____

_____

Recipes:

Are there certain dishes that remind you of childhood family holidays? Describe. _____

_____

_____

_____

_____

_____

What's the first dish you learned how to cook? How did you learn? _____

_____

_____

_____

_____

_____

Is there a dish that was the bane of your existence as a child? Did you ever argue with your parents over eating it? Who won? _____

_____

_____

_____

_____

_____

What was your typical after-school snack? _____

_____

_____

_____

_____

Mementos:

Do you have any mementos of your time at camp? What are they? How do they remind you of your camp experience?

_____

_____

_____

_____

_____

_____

_____

What's your most treasured souvenir from a family vacation? Why? _____

_____

_____

_____

_____

_____

_____

_____

Do you have any mementos that were given to you as going away presents when you moved? What were they? Who gave them to you? _____

_____

_____

_____

_____

_____

_____

The Interviews Method

If you've hit upon a topic you'd like to explore further or aren't sure your memory serves you correctly, you might want to interview people who knew you as a kid. Choose interview candidates from The Usual Suspects list below, or identify a few candidates of your own. Their accounts can help broaden your perspective and ground your story in fact. Be sure to ask your interview subjects in advance if they can spare an hour for the interview—that way they won't get testy halfway through, and you'll get much better material. The Sample Interview Questions included below should get your interview rolling.

The Usual Suspects

Friends
Neighbors
Elementary school classmates
Teachers
Parents, foster or adoptive parents, and stepparents
Grandparents
Relatives
Coaches
Teammates
Fellow campers, Boy Scouts, Girl Scouts, etc.
Camp counselors
Daycare providers
School play director
Choir leader
Librarians, shopkeepers, and others in your hometown who knew you back then
Others: _____

Sample Interview Questions

Here are six interview questions to get you started—feel free to supplement or replace these questions with your own. You may want to record the interview on a voice recorder, and jot down the most interesting quotes here later on. Keep in mind that a single question can take 5-10 minutes to answer, depending on how chatty your interviewee is and whether you ask follow-up questions.

I remember that you were there when I _____ as a kid. What do you remember about that time? _____

_____

_____

_____

How would you describe me as a child? _____

_____

_____

_____

What activities did I seem most interested in when I was a kid? _____

_____

_____

_____

Can you tell me what people, subjects, and activities seemed to be my favorites back then? _____

_____

_____

_____

Was there a particular move, trip, or event that seemed to affect me deeply as a child? _____

_____
_____
_____

How did I seem similar to other kids you knew, and how did I seem different? _____

_____
_____
_____

_____
_____
_____
_____
_____
_____
_____
_____
_____
_____
_____
_____
_____
_____
_____
_____
_____

_____
_____
_____
_____
_____
_____
_____
_____
_____
_____
_____
_____
_____
_____
_____
_____
_____
_____
_____
_____
_____
_____
_____
_____
_____
_____
_____
_____
_____
_____
_____

ADOLESCENCE

Think back...

Say the word "adolescence" in a crowd of people, and someone is bound to cringe. Try it: you'll notice that even former star athletes, class presidents, and prom queens are not immune. Truth is, almost everyone's golden teenage years contain tarnished, awkward moments—if not entire days spent memorizing the words to sappy pop songs, and month after month of unfortunate hairstyles.

This creates a problem for the autobiographer. While we're in our teens, we can be so intent on getting them over and done with that the day-to-day details elude us. So when we try to recollect our teen years, it can take awhile to push past the overwhelming sense of relief that they're over, and get down to specifics.

When we do remember telling teen moments, the urge to laugh them off quickly can be overpowering. Resist it. Your adolescence is worth more than a cheap laugh. Just take a look at all those teen comedies gathering dust on the shelves of your local video store; do you really want your life story to become *that* dated, *that* quickly? If you dare to reveal the anguish and triumph behind your antics, you could have a timeless comedy on your hands. It worked for Shakespeare, and it can work for you. And if your adolescence was truly tragic, tell it like it is—or as Shakespeare would put it, "to thine own self be true."

As you unravel the tangle of your teenage years, you may come across some knots that are especially difficult to undo. Why did you stop being friends with that person? Why did you gain and lose interest in basketball? Why did you make fun of that kid in math class? Probably you don't remember your adolescent motives very well; maybe you were never all that conscious of them in the first place. But try to work through these tricky questions, rather than around them—in that knotted mess, you could find a thread that weaves its way through your entire life story.

Forge ahead!

Where to begin? Anywhere you want—growth spurts, your first communion or bar mitzvah, when your voice broke during your choir solo or you had your first period in P.E. class. Basically, whenever you feel you wound up in the throes of adolescence. Write until you think you're starting to delve into your coming of age memories; that's a sign you're ready for the next chapter.

Below are three methods to get your memories out of your subconscious, and onto paper where they belong. These are Q&A, Artifacts, and Interviews. Try one method that comes naturally, and one that challenges you—it'll enrich your autobiography, and your experience of writing it too.

The Q&A Method

Jot down your responses to at least a few of the questions that seem relevant to you under each of the four main topics: Responsibilities, Trouble, Awkwardness, and Romance. Feel free to add others or go off on tangents as the spirit moves you. If you find yourself hesitating, you might try reading the questions aloud and recording your spoken answers with a voice recorder. Then as you play back your recording, write down the interesting parts of your answers and elaborate on them as you see fit. Your answers should bring your adolescence into focus, and provide a few juicy anecdotes besides.

Q&A Topic #1: Responsibilities

Chores

What chores did you have to do at home—cleaning, cooking, doing the dishes, pet care, mowing the lawn? _____

_____

_____

_____

_____

_____

_____

_____

Which chores did you dread? Which ones were somehow satisfying? _____

_____

_____

_____

_____

_____

_____

_____

Did you ever try to weasel your way out of doing a chore? Describe. Did it work? _____

_____

_____

_____

_____

_____

_____

_____

Jobs

Did you have a paid job in your teens? Doing what? How much did you make? _____

_____

_____

_____

_____

_____

How did you spend your paycheck? _____

_____

_____

_____

_____

_____

Did you get along with your boss? Explain. _____

_____

_____

_____

_____

Which co-workers did you particularly like? Dislike? Why?

_____

_____

_____

_____

Childcare

Did you ever babysit? For whom? _____

_____
_____
_____
_____

What were the kids like? _____

_____
_____
_____
_____

Did you or the kids ever do something you had to hide from their parents? What? _____

_____
_____
_____
_____

Did you ever look after your siblings? Did they give you a hard time? _____

_____
_____
_____
_____

Did you take to this parenting role? Why or why not? __

_____
_____
_____

Grades

What kind of grades did you get in high school? _____

_____

_____

_____

_____

How important were grades to you? Why? _____

_____

_____

_____

_____

Did you ever cheat to make the grade? Cram for tests? Describe. _____

_____

_____

_____

_____

Did you have a tutor for certain subjects? Which ones? What was that like? _____

_____

_____

_____

Did you ever tutor someone else? Who? What did you get out of the experience? _____

_____

_____

_____

Teams and Organizations

Did you participate in sports? Describe. _____

_____

_____

_____

_____

_____

_____

Were you on any teams? What did you like or dislike about belonging to each team? _____

_____

_____

_____

_____

_____

Did you join any student clubs or organizations? Which ones? _____

_____

_____

_____

_____

_____

What did you get out of being in each group? _____

_____

_____

_____

_____

_____

Did you belong to a religious youth group? Describe. _____

_____

_____

_____

_____

_____

_____

What about community groups or volunteer organizations?
Describe. _____

_____

_____

_____

_____

_____

Of all the groups you belonged to, which one made you feel
most proud to be a member? _____

_____

_____

_____

_____

_____

Which did you enjoy the most? Which did you enjoy the
least? _____

_____

_____

_____

_____

_____

Other responsibilities

Describe. _____

_____

_____

_____

_____

_____

How did you feel about them? _____

_____

_____

_____

_____

_____

_____

_____

_____

_____

_____

_____

_____

_____

_____

_____

_____

Parents and Family

How late was your curfew? Did you ever break it? Describe.

_____

_____

_____

_____

_____

Did your parent(s) ever go away overnight and leave you in charge? What happened? _____

_____

_____

_____

_____

_____

Were you allowed to use the family car? Did you ever abuse the privilege? _____

_____

_____

_____

_____

_____

Did you ever get in major trouble with your parent(s)? How? What did you learn from the experience? _____

_____

_____

_____

School

Did you ever flunk a class or test in high school? Which one(s)? _____

_____

_____

_____

Did you ever get into a fistfight or shouting match at school? Describe. _____

_____

_____

_____

Were you ever suspended from school? Why? _____

_____

_____

_____

Legal

Did you ever have a brush with the law as a teenager? Describe. _____

_____

_____

_____

Was there anyone among your friends or in your family that got into trouble with the law? How did that affect you at the time? _____

_____

_____

_____

Were you ever at a party that got out of control, and the police were called? Describe. What did you do when the cops showed up? _____

_____

_____

_____

Did you ever have to go to court or jail for any reason? Why? What was the outcome? Has the experience had any lasting effect on you? _____

_____

_____

_____

Other trouble

Describe. _____

_____

_____

_____

_____

_____

_____

_____

_____

_____

_____

_____

_____

_____

_____

_____

Q&A Topic #3: Awkwardness

Social gaffes

Did you ever embarrass yourself in front of a crowd of people? How? Was there someone who just wouldn't let you live it down? Who? _____

_____

_____

_____

_____

_____

_____

Can you recall a time when you had the opportunity to shine, and goofed it up? Describe. Why do you think that happened? _____

_____

_____

_____

_____

_____

_____

Did you ever let a comment slip out that shocked or hurt someone else? Describe. Did you try to make amends? How? _____

_____

_____

_____

_____

_____

_____

Fitting in

Did you go out of your way to fit in or stand out in high school? What was it about you that stood out in a crowd, even if you didn't want it to? _____

_____

_____

_____

_____

_____

How did you deal with the various social cliques in your high school? Did you belong to a clique? _____

_____

_____

_____

_____

Do you remember consciously trying to dress or act like someone else? Who? Did you have any habits or mannerisms other people around you copied? Why? _____

_____

_____

_____

_____

Did being cool matter to you? How did you determine what was cool, and what wasn't? _____

_____

_____

_____

_____

Was it important to you to be popular? Why or why not?

_____
_____
_____
_____
_____
_____

Can you think of a time you could've gone along with the
crowd, but choose not to? Describe. _____

_____
_____
_____
_____
_____
_____

Was there anything you desperately wanted to change about
yourself? What? _____

_____
_____
_____
_____
_____

What were your nicknames in high school? Why? _____

_____
_____
_____
_____
_____

Fashion victim

How would you describe your signature style in high school? _____

_____

_____

_____

_____

As a teen, did you ever go along with a fashion trend that you knew was wrong for you? Describe. _____

_____

_____

_____

How did you wear your hair back then? What about make-up? _____

_____

_____

_____

Did you ever dream about owning a certain item of clothing that now seems ridiculous to you? _____

_____

_____

_____

When you think of what you wore to school dances, how does it make you feel? _____

_____

_____

_____

Flubs

Were you ever caught in a white lie? Describe. _____

_____

_____

_____

_____

_____

Ever pretend to be somebody you weren't in order to impress other people? Explain. Was the real you exposed? How? _____

_____

_____

_____

_____

Can you recall pretending to know something you didn't, and getting called on it publicly? Describe. _____

_____

_____

_____

_____

_____

Other awkward moments

Describe. How did it affect you at the time? _____

_____

_____

_____

_____

_____

Crushes

How long did your typical high school crush last? _____

_____
_____
_____
_____
_____

Who did you have a crush on for the longest time? Why? Did you tell that person? What was the response? _____

_____
_____
_____
_____
_____

Did you ever send notes or gifts signed "A Secret Admirer"? To whom? What was the response? Was your identity discovered? How? _____

_____
_____
_____
_____

Did you have pictures in your locker or posters in your room of celebrities you dreamed about dating? Which ones? __

_____
_____
_____
_____

School dances

Did you usually go to school dances, or avoid them? Why?

_____

_____

_____

_____

_____

_____

What was the best time you ever had at a school dance? What about the worst time? Describe. _____

_____

_____

_____

_____

_____

Can you remember being nervous about meeting your date's parents? Describe. _____

_____

_____

_____

_____

_____

Did you ever go stag? What was it like? _____

_____

_____

_____

_____

_____

First kiss

What three words best describe your first kiss? _____

_____

_____

_____

_____

_____

Who was it you kissed? Where did it take place? _____

_____

_____

_____

_____

Did you bump teeth or lock braces? Describe. _____

_____

_____

_____

_____

Were you caught in the act? Explain. _____

_____

_____

_____

_____

What do you think that person remembers about the kiss?

_____

_____

_____

_____

Dating

Did you date much as a teenager? Why or why not? _____

_____

_____

_____

_____

_____

_____

Can you name all the people you dated—first and last names? _____

_____

_____

_____

_____

_____

_____

Who did your parent(s) approve of most? Why? _____

_____

_____

_____

_____

_____

Who did your parent(s) approve of the least? Why? _____

_____

_____

_____

_____

_____

What was your best date as a teenager? What about your worst? _____

_____

_____

_____

_____

Did you date someone of another race or faith? _____

_____

_____

_____

_____

Were you ever set up with a date by friends or relatives? How was that? _____

_____

_____

_____

_____

Did you ever have to break up with someone? How did you do it? Describe. _____

_____

_____

_____

_____

Did anyone ever break up with you? How did you react?

_____

_____

_____

The Artifacts Method

To bring your memories to the surface, try digging up a few souvenirs of your teenage years. Pick a few items from the lists below to examine, and use the accompanying questions as a guide to further discoveries. If you pay close attention to these objects, you'll find they have a lot to say about the adolescent you once were—and the person you now are.

Notes passed in class and letters/postcards received or sent as a teen:

Are there stickers, doodles, or drawings on them? Describe.

_____

_____

_____

_____

Do they contain secret codes, inside jokes, or slang you and your friends invented? Explain. _____

_____

_____

_____

What are the recurring topics in them? _____

_____

_____

_____

Why do you think you've kept them all these years? _____

_____

_____

_____

Official high school memorabilia (yearbooks, school newspapers, prom photos, etc.):

What do you look like in your yearbook photo(s)? Describe.

_____

_____

_____

_____

_____

_____

If you included a motto in your yearbook, what was it? Does that motto still apply? _____

_____

_____

_____

_____

_____

Who signed your yearbook, and what did they say about you? _____

_____

_____

_____

_____

What does your prom photo look like? What can you remember about having that photo taken? _____

_____

_____

_____

_____

Music you listened to as a teen:

What kind of music did you listen to most often? What were your favorite albums? _____

_____

_____

_____

_____

_____

What songs do you credit with getting you through tough times as a teen? _____

_____

_____

_____

_____

_____

Did you hang out with other kids that listened to the same type of music? _____

_____

_____

_____

_____

_____

Can you recall what you thought of kids who listened to other types of music? _____

_____

_____

_____

_____

Posters and photos that decorated your room or school locker:

What inspirational quotes did you have up in your locker or room? Do these still apply? _____

_____

_____

_____

_____

_____

Did you have pennants or posters with your school name?

_____

_____

_____

_____

_____

What posters or photos of teen heartthrobs did you own? Describe. _____

_____

_____

_____

_____

_____

What other kinds of posters or art decorated your room and locker? Describe. _____

_____

_____

_____

_____

Clothes and jewelry you wore in your teens:

Can you describe your favorite outfit as a teen? _____

_____

_____

_____

_____

_____

Do you still have any of the clothes you wore as a teen? Which ones? _____

_____

_____

_____

_____

_____

How would you describe the different fashion phases you went through as a teen? _____

_____

_____

_____

_____

_____

Did you have to wear a school uniform? How did you feel about it? _____

_____

_____

_____

_____

_____

Books and magazines you read in high school:

Were there any books you particularly related to as a teen? Why? _____

_____

_____

_____

_____

_____

Which magazines do you remember poring over as a teen? Why? What do you think of them now? _____

_____

_____

_____

_____

_____

High school athletic gear:

What high school team T-shirts or sweatshirts do you still have in your closet? Why? _____

_____

_____

_____

_____

Did you ever earn a letter jacket or sweater? What did that mean to you? _____

_____

_____

_____

_____

Programs or ticket stubs from plays, concerts, musicals, competitions, or dance performances:

What was the first concert you ever attended? Do you still have the ticket stub or program? _____

_____

_____

_____

What do you remember most about these shows? _____

_____

_____

_____

Does your name appear in any of the programs? Which ones? Why? _____

_____

_____

_____

Gifts you gave, made, or received as a teen:

Did your parent(s) save any cards or gifts you made as a teen? Describe. _____

_____

_____

_____

What gift were you most glad to receive? Why? Is that gift still the kind of thing you value today? _____

_____

_____

_____

Item(s) you bought with money you earned as a teen:

How long did you hanker after this item before you finally bought it? _____

_____

_____

_____

_____

_____

How did you earn the money to buy it? Was it worth it?

_____

_____

_____

_____

_____

_____

Other:

Describe. _____

_____

_____

_____

_____

_____

_____

_____

_____

_____

_____

The Interviews Method

If you've hit upon a topic you'd like to explore further or aren't sure your memory serves you correctly, you might want to interview people who knew you as a teenager. Choose interview candidates from The Usual Suspects list below, or identify a few candidates of your own. Their accounts can help broaden your perspective and ground your story in fact. Be sure to ask your interview subjects in advance if they can spare an hour for the interview—that way they won't get testy halfway through, and you'll get much better material. The Sample Interview Questions included below should get your interview rolling.

The Usual Suspects

High school classmates

Teachers

First loves (don't be shy—writing your autobiography gives you a legitimate reason to contact almost anyone!)

Parents

Siblings

Teammates

Fellow participants in extracurricular activities (plays, band, yearbook, etc.)

Community members (teen center volunteers, youth group leaders, etc.)

Others: _____

Sample Interview Questions

Here are six interview questions to get you started—feel

free to supplement or replace these questions with your own. You may want to record the interview on a voice recorder, and jot down the most interesting quotes here later on. Keep in mind that a single question can take 5-10 minutes to answer, depending on how chatty your interviewee is and whether you ask follow-up questions.

I remember that you were there when I _____ as a teenager. What do you remember about that time? ____

_____

_____

_____

_____

How would you describe me as a teenager? _____

_____

_____

_____

_____

What five words always seemed to crop up in our conversations back then? _____

_____

_____

_____

Can you tell me what one outfit I always wore, or what album I always listened to? _____

_____

_____

_____

Could you tell me what movie, book or crush I couldn't stop talking about as a teenager? _____

_____

_____

_____

How did I seem similar to other teenagers you knew, and how did I seem different? _____

_____

_____

_____

_____

_____

_____

_____

_____

_____

_____

_____

_____

_____

_____

_____

_____

_____

_____

_____

COMING OF AGE

Think back...

In theory, the passage from adolescence to adulthood is a well-traveled highway with plenty of signposts: your growth spurt tapers off here, you reach voting age there, graduate high school next exit, strike out on your own after that, then go to college and/or get a job. But in reality, most of us veer off the road at some point. We wind up on foot whacking our way through brambles, and arrive at maturity by following our intuition. So when you write your coming of age story, tell it like the adventure that it was—don't stick to the official map of the experience.

Try to retrace your steps to adulthood. Was there a crisis, relationship, historical event, mentor, or book that set or changed the course of your life? Start with those, but don't stop there. This is your autobiography, not an award acceptance speech—you can do more here than recite the obligatory list of influences and mentors. Write also about wrong turns you took, times when you felt lost, and obstacles you thought you'd never overcome; these help you and your readers understand the adult you've become.

"But I don't always qualify as an adult," you sheepishly admit. "I've still got a lot of growing up to do." Join the club. Lots of us adults are only kids who've mastered a passable impersonation of a grown-up—but it takes a mature individual indeed to own up to that fact in an autobiography. So be honest: did learning that grown-up behavior take you a couple of years, or a couple of decades? And were all those lessons really necessary? Some adolescent behavior is better left behind you, but sometimes youthful enthusiasm serves you well. Your task as an autobiographer—and an adult—is to tell these two instances apart.

Forge ahead!
Where to begin? Anywhere you want—declarations of independence, dealing with roommates, landing your first unbelievably rewarding/soul-crushingly dull job. Basically, whenever you feel you got cracking on adulthood. Write until you think you're starting to delve into your memories of coming into your own; that's a sign you're ready for the next chapter.

Below are three methods to get your memories out of your subconscious, and onto paper where they belong. These are Q&A, Artifacts, and Interviews. Try one method that comes naturally, and at least one that challenges you— it'll enrich your autobiography, and your experience of writing it too.

The Q&A Method
Jot down your responses to at least a few of the questions that seem relevant to you under each of the four main topics: Convictions, Encouragement, Influences, and Independence. Feel free to add others or go off on tangents as the spirit moves you. If you find yourself hesitating, you might try reading the questions aloud and recording your spoken answers with a voice recorder. Then as you play back your recording, write down the interesting parts of your answers and elaborate on them as you see fit. Your answers should bring your coming of age story into focus, and provide a few juicy anecdotes besides.

Q&A Topic #1: Convictions
Ethical dilemmas

Can you remember a time in early adulthood that you got yourself out of trouble by telling a little white lie? Can you recall telling a lie to get someone else out of trouble? Describe. How little was that white lie, really? _____

_____

_____

_____

_____

Do you remember breaking a rule or law you thought was wrong? What one? _____

_____

_____

_____

_____

Did you ever choose the lesser of two evils because finding an alternate solution seemed like too much trouble? Explain. _____

_____

_____

_____

_____

Can you recall a time when you had an opportunity to get ahead at someone else's expense? What did you do? ____

_____

_____

_____

Political leanings

What was the biggest argument you had about politics during your young adult years? _____

_____

_____

_____

_____

_____

What's the first political organization or party you ever joined, and why? _____

_____

_____

_____

_____

_____

Can you recall speaking out publicly on a political issue? Describe. What kind of response did you get? _____

_____

_____

_____

_____

_____

Did you volunteer for a campaign or political cause back then? Which one(s)? Why? _____

_____

_____

_____

_____

Religious beliefs

What influence did your religion have over the choices you
made in your early adulthood? _____

_____

_____

_____

_____

_____

Which of your family's religious practices did you keep after
you left home? Which ones did you drop? Why? _____

_____

_____

_____

_____

_____

Did you date someone outside your faith? Who? How did
the relationship end? _____

_____

_____

_____

_____

_____

Were you ever called upon to defend your beliefs publicly?
Explain. _____

_____

_____

_____

_____

Q&A Topic #2: Encouragement

Role models

Who did you admire most? Why? _____

_____

_____

_____

_____

_____

_____

_____

Did you think of your parent(s) or sibling(s) as role models?
Why or why not? _____

_____

_____

_____

_____

_____

_____

_____

Did you collect writings, albums, or artwork by any one person in particular back then? Why do you think you identified so strongly with that person? _____

_____

_____

_____

_____

_____

_____

_____

Memorable advice

What inspirational quotes did you have up in your room or apartment back then? _____

_____

_____

_____

_____

_____

What would you say was your personal motto at the time?

_____

_____

_____

_____

_____

What's the best piece of advice you ever received about growing up? _____

_____

_____

_____

_____

_____

What advice or criticism did you receive from someone you respected that was initially hard to swallow, but ultimately proved constructive? _____

_____

_____

_____

_____

Big breaks

What was your first opportunity to do something that genuinely excited and challenged you? _____

_____

_____

_____

_____

_____

How many disappointments had you experienced before this opportunity came your way? Describe. _____

_____

_____

_____

_____

_____

How did you land your first job? Who were your references?

_____

_____

_____

_____

_____

_____

Who was there to congratulate you when you made it, and reassure you when you didn't? _____

_____

_____

_____

_____

Recognition

Did you earn any promotions, status or recognition rare for someone of your age and experience? How did you deal with the high expectations that went with it? _____

_____

_____

_____

_____

_____

_____

_____

_____

How did the recognition you received affect your relationship to your family or community? _____

_____

_____

_____

_____

_____

_____

_____

Did you make strides in your chosen career? Describe. __

_____

_____

_____

_____

_____

_____

_____

Relationships

Did you ever ask a total stranger out on a date? Describe.

_____

_____

_____

_____

_____

_____

_____

_____

Have you ever been the first person in a relationship to use the L-word? How did you feel about it? _____

_____

_____

_____

_____

_____

_____

_____

_____

Do you remember the first time your heart was broken? How did you get over it? _____

_____

_____

_____

_____

_____

_____

Q&A Topic #3: Influences
College classes

What class assignment was most memorable for you? Why?

_____

_____

_____

_____

_____

_____

Can you recall being so captivated by a subject you covered in class that you studied the topic independently, or pursued it in your career? _____

_____

_____

_____

_____

Did you ever have a teacher who gave you advice or feedback that proved especially helpful? What was it? _____

_____

_____

_____

_____

Do you still stay in touch with a teacher or other students from any of your classes? Which ones? Why? _____

_____

_____

_____

_____

Books

Which books were you determined to get through, even though they were challenging? What did you get out of reading them? _____

_____
_____
_____
_____

Did you ever stay up reading a book all night when you knew you had class or work the next morning? Which book? What do you remember about it? _____

_____
_____
_____
_____

Can you recall getting into a heated discussion over any book back then? With whom? Why? What was the upshot?

_____
_____
_____
_____

Can you recall being hit with a sudden realization about your life while reading a book? What was the book? What was the realization? _____

_____
_____
_____
_____

Music and Art

Can you remember what songs were most popular in those days? Were there any you particularly liked or disliked? Why? _____

_____

_____

_____

_____

_____

What albums did you listen to most often back then? What concerts did you go to? _____

_____

_____

_____

_____

_____

Were you ever stopped in your tracks by a work of art? Which one? How did it make you feel? _____

_____

_____

_____

_____

Did you go to see dance, theater or art shows much? Why were you so interested or uninterested in shows then? __

_____

_____

_____

_____

Movies

What movies were released in the years when you were coming of age? Which ones can you recall in detail? Why?

_____

_____

_____

_____

_____

Did any films you saw seem to mirror your own experience at that time? Which ones? How? _____

_____

_____

_____

_____

_____

Did you ever quote from any movies in those days? Which ones, and why? _____

_____

_____

_____

_____

_____

Other

Describe. _____

_____

_____

_____

_____

Q&A Topic #4: Independence
Roommates

Did you have roommates? How did you find them? _____

_____

_____

_____

_____

_____

_____

What did you have in common with them at the time? __

_____

_____

_____

_____

_____

How were you different from one another? _____

_____

_____

_____

_____

_____

How did you get along? Give an example of a typical interaction between you. _____

_____

_____

_____

_____

_____

Your own place

Where was it? Describe the building. What neighborhood was it in? _____

_____

_____

_____

_____

Did you get to know any of your neighbors? What were they like? _____

_____

_____

_____

What's the worst smell that ever originated from inside your apartment? Explain. _____

_____

_____

_____

What's the worst household disaster you experienced? How did you handle it? _____

_____

_____

_____

Did you ever have houseguests that wore out their welcome? Describe. _____

_____

_____

_____

First full-time job

How did you land your first job? What can you remember about your job interview? _____

_____

_____

_____

_____

What was a typical workday like for you? _____

_____

_____

_____

_____

Did you make friends at work? With whom? How? ____

_____

_____

_____

_____

What was your boss like? How'd you get along? _____

_____

_____

_____

_____

If you've since moved on, why did you leave that job? ____

_____

_____

_____

_____

First car

What kind of car was it? How did you choose that particular car? How much did it cost? _____

_____

_____

_____

_____

_____

Did you customize it with a rearview mirror ornament, dashboard décor, stereo system, or paint job? Describe. __

_____

_____

_____

_____

_____

What's the longest road trip you ever took in it? Describe.

_____

_____

_____

_____

_____

How long did you have that car? Why did you get rid of it? Do you know what happened to it after you got rid of it?

_____

_____

_____

_____

_____

The Artifacts Method

To bring your memories to the surface, try digging up a few souvenirs of your early adulthood. Pick at least three items from the list below to examine, and use the accompanying questions as a guide to further discoveries. If you pay close attention to these objects, you'll find they have a lot to say about the person you once were—and the person you now are.

Letters, cards, e-mails, commentary and other input from teachers, mentors, and role models:

What pieces of advice or encouragement can you remember verbatim, without even having to look at the letter or note containing it? _____

_____

_____

_____

_____

What papers have you saved because of the comments your professor wrote on it? Do you remember how you initially responded to this input? _____

_____

_____

_____

Do you have any congratulatory cards sent to you by a teacher, mentor on the occasion of some personal triumph? Who was it from? What does it say? _____

_____

_____

_____

Political paraphernalia (T-shirts, news clippings, bumper stickers, buttons, and other campaign or cause-related memorabilia):

Have you saved a lot of mementos from any one political campaign or cause in particular? Why were you so attached to that campaign or cause? _____

_____

_____

_____

_____

Do you recall someone responding to your bumper sticker? Describe. _____

_____

_____

_____

_____

Books you read back then:

Which book is especially dog-eared, because you dragged it around with you all over the place? Why was that book so important to you at the time? _____

_____

_____

_____

What parts of your book did you underline? Did you make any notes in the margins? _____

_____

_____

_____

Your favorite music at the time:

Can you recall the effect a musical album or song had on you when you first heard it? Describe. _____

_____

_____

_____

Did an album serve as a soundtrack to some major event in your early adulthood? Is there a particular person you associate with this album? Explain. _____

_____

_____

_____

Can you still remember the lyrics? What lyrics do you remember finding especially poignant at the time? _____

_____

_____

_____

Programs, ticket stubs, postcards or show catalogs (from art exhibits, dance or theater performances, movies and concerts):

What do you remember most about going to this show?

_____

_____

Were you involved in this show, either in the spotlight or behind the scenes? How? _____

_____

_____

Photos of your first apartment and roommates, plus any photos you had on your fridge back then:

Who are the people in the photo? What was your relationship to them? What does this photo capture about them?

_____

_____

_____

_____

Can you recall which photos won pride of place on your fridge, and why? _____

_____

_____

_____

_____

Stuff you "borrowed" from roommates, plus any recipes, furniture, and knick-knacks that date back to your first apartment/house:

How many moves has this particular item survived? Did you ever think about leaving it behind? What made you change your mind? _____

_____

_____

_____

For stuff you borrowed—what made you risk the wrath of your roomie and keep it? _____

_____

_____

_____

Religious items (religious symbols or texts, items used or displayed on religious holidays, and icons, rosaries, rugs, and other items used during prayer):

Did you often wear or display symbols of your faith as a young adult? Why or why not? _____

_____

_____

_____

If you don't consider yourself very religious, why do you think you've kept these religious items all these years? __

_____

_____

Can you remember reading any of the religious texts? Which ones? _____

_____

_____

Anything you wrote at the time (letters to friends and family, poetry, senior thesis, letters to the editor, short stories and applications to jobs or schools):

What subjects are raised most often in your writings? What got you interested in those subjects? _____

_____

_____

When you read your old writing now, whose influence can you see clearly? _____

_____

_____

The Interviews Method

If you've hit upon a topic you'd like to explore further or aren't sure your memory serves you correctly, you might want to interview people who knew you when you were coming of age. Choose interview candidates from The Usual Suspects list below, or identify a few candidates of your own. Their accounts can help broaden your perspective and ground your story in fact. Be sure to ask your interview subjects in advance if they can spare an hour for the interview—that way they won't get testy halfway through, and you'll get much better material. The Sample Interview Questions included below should get your interview rolling.

The Usual Suspects

Friends
Teachers
Mentors
Religious leaders
Roommates
College classmates
Bosses
Co-workers
Parents
Siblings
Love interests
Relatives
Fellow volunteers (political campaigns, social causes, charities, etc.)
Others: _____

Sample Interview Questions

Here are six interview questions to get you started—feel free to supplement or replace these questions with your own. You may want to record the interview on a voice recorder, and jot down the most interesting quotes here later on. Keep in mind that a single question can take 5-10 minutes to answer, depending on how chatty your interviewee is and whether you ask follow-up questions.

I remember that you were there when I _____ back then. What do you remember about that time? _____

_____

_____

_____

How would you describe me when I was coming of age?

_____

_____

_____

What five words always seemed to crop up in our conversations back then? _____

_____

_____

_____

Can you tell me what one book, album or movie I always referred to? _____

_____

_____

_____

Could you tell me what political issue, personal or career crisis I seemed most concerned about back then? _____

_____

_____

_____

How did I seem similar to other people you knew that were my age, and how did I seem different? _____

_____

_____

_____

_____

_____

_____

_____

_____

_____

_____

_____

_____

_____

_____

_____

_____

_____

_____

_____

_____

COMING INTO YOUR OWN

Think back...

When we're kids, we expect a coming of age story to end in a swift, decisive happily ever after—but as grown-ups, we know better. If a movie ended in such an anticlimactic way, we'd feel cheated; we'd know we were just being set up for a sequel. Once we've witnessed characters being built during the trials of early adulthood, we want to find out what happens to them when left to their own devices.

So this is your big break—your chance to be not just the star of your story, but also its director. Try to focus on what you made happen, not just what happened to you. How did you approach life's trials and adventures? What moments of triumph or resolution did you achieve? And since our life stories are truly ensemble pieces, who did you choose as your supporting cast?

Forge ahead!

Where to begin? Anywhere you want—a stroke of genius, an ethical dilemma, hosting a family holiday, or getting stranded atop Machu Picchu with a cranky llama (which might not actually feel so different to you from that family holiday). Basically, whenever you feel you finally got the hang of adulthood. Write until you think you're starting to delve into stories of self-realization; that's a sign you're ready for the next chapter.

Below are three methods to get your memories out of your subconscious, and onto paper where they belong. These are Q&A, Artifacts, and Interviews. Try one method that comes naturally, and one that challenges you—it'll enrich your autobiography, and your experience of writing it too.

The Q&A Method

*Jot down your responses to at least a few of the questions that seem relevant to you under each of the four main topics: **Trials, Breakthroughs, Community and Adventure**. Feel free to add others or go off on tangents as the spirit moves you. If you find yourself hesitating, you might try reading the questions aloud and recording your spoken answers with a voice recorder. Then as you play back your recording, write down the interesting parts of your answers and elaborate on them as you see fit. Your answers should bring your adult experience into focus, and provide a few juicy anecdotes besides.*

Q&A Topic #1: Trials
Relationships/Family

If you have a life partner, how did you two meet? What was it about this person that led you to conclude that this was the one for you? _____

_____

_____

_____

_____

_____

Do you have children? How did your life change when you had your first child? _____

_____

_____

_____

_____

If you were to brag about your children, what would you say about each of them? _____

_____
_____
_____
_____
_____
_____
_____
_____

If you were to confess your hopes for each of them, what would they be? _____

_____
_____
_____
_____
_____
_____
_____
_____

What would you say was your single biggest challenge as a parent? _____

_____
_____
_____
_____
_____
_____
_____

How would you describe your relationship to your parent(s)? How did it change when you became an adult?

_____

_____

_____

_____

_____

Are you an aunt or an uncle? Describe your role in the life of your niece or nephew. _____

_____

_____

_____

_____

_____

Was your relationship with any extended relations ever strained or strengthened by some event? What was it? __

_____

_____

_____

_____

Is there anyone in your life you've adopted as a family member? How did that happen? _____

_____

_____

_____

_____

_____

Have you had any particularly tumultuous relationships as an adult? How did you work through them, or put them behind you? _____

_____

_____

_____

_____

_____

Have you ever been estranged from a relative as an adult? Who? Why? _____

_____

_____

_____

_____

Have you ever looked after an ill or disabled relative or friend? Describe. How did it change your relationship? How did it change you? _____

_____

_____

_____

_____

Have you ever lost a close friend or relative? Is there something you would've liked to tell that person, but never got a chance to say? _____

_____

_____

_____

_____

Is there anyone from this time of your life who you would avoid if you noticed that person on the street? Who? Why?

_____

_____

_____

_____

_____

_____

Did you go through any particularly difficult breakups? Why were these breakups so hard on you? _____

_____

_____

_____

_____

_____

Have you ever been divorced or legally separated? _____

_____

_____

_____

_____

_____

If you had a significant other during these years, what would you say was the toughest test of your relationship? What was the outcome? _____

_____

_____

_____

_____

Friends

Do you have one primary circle of friends, or several different ones? How would you describe your circle(s)? _____

_____

_____

_____

_____

_____

_____

_____

_____

Do you have friends that you've known for a decade or more? What phases have you seen one another through?

_____

_____

_____

_____

_____

_____

_____

With what friend do you have the most worthwhile arguments? Give an example of such an argument. _____

_____

_____

_____

_____

_____

_____

_____

Which friends can you count on to share your happiness when things go your way? _____

_____

_____

_____

_____

_____

Do you still keep in touch with people from your former workplace(s)? Why or why not? _____

_____

_____

_____

_____

_____

Which neighbors would notice when you're gone for a week? Why? Which neighbors' absence would you notice most? Why? _____

_____

_____

_____

_____

_____

Which of your neighbors do you know best, and why? __

_____

_____

_____

_____

_____

Values

Have you ever done something that was against your moral or religious beliefs? What was it? How did you come to terms with it? _____

_____
_____
_____
_____
_____

Is there a social issue that you've made it a personal priority to address? Explain. _____

_____
_____
_____
_____
_____

Did you ever hide or deny your religion, political beliefs, or sexual orientation? What was the outcome? _____

_____
_____
_____
_____
_____

Have you ever knowingly broken the law? Why? _____

_____
_____
_____
_____

Have you had an affair while you were in a committed relationship? What happened? _____

_____

_____

_____

_____

_____

Did you ever cheat on your taxes? How? _____

_____

_____

_____

_____

_____

Have you ever done something you thought was wrong as a favor for a friend? Explain. _____

_____

_____

_____

_____

_____

Can you recall being asked by someone in a position of power over you to do something you knew was wrong? What was it? What did you do? _____

_____

_____

_____

_____

_____

Did you ever tell on someone for doing something you felt was wrong or unfair? What was it? How did you feel about it afterward? _____

_____

_____

_____

_____

_____

_____

Have you ever taken credit for something that you didn't do? What was it? _____

_____

_____

_____

_____

_____

_____

Have you worked for an organization you knew had unethical business dealings? How long? Why did you finally leave? _____

_____

_____

_____

_____

_____

_____

Health

Has maintaining good health been a struggle for you? In what way? What has motivated you to become more aware of your health? _____

_____

_____

_____

_____

_____

_____

Have you ever been diagnosed with a serious illness? What was your immediate response to the news? What specific advice or show of support did you find particularly helpful in dealing with it? _____

_____

_____

_____

_____

_____

Has a friend or relative of yours ever been diagnosed with a terminal illness? How did you find out about it, and how did you respond? _____

_____

_____

_____

_____

Did you ever endanger your health with crash diets or other irregular eating patterns? How did you address the underlying causes of this behavior? _____

_____

_____

_____

_____

_____

Is there a time in your adult life when you drank heavily or used drugs on a regular basis? Describe. How have your drinking habits or drug use changed? _____

_____

_____

_____

_____

_____

Were you ever in therapy? Describe. _____

_____

_____

_____

_____

_____

Have you ever been debilitated by depression? How did you deal with your depression? _____

_____

_____

_____

_____

Career

How many jobs have you had? What places have you worked? _____

_____

_____

_____

_____

_____

What career achievements make you feel most proud? Why? _____

_____

_____

_____

_____

_____

Can you think of a time you succeeded when others didn't expect you would? Describe. _____

_____

_____

_____

_____

_____

What's the most satisfying job you've ever had? Did you make money? _____

_____

_____

_____

_____

Have you ever wanted a job you didn't get? How did you handle the disappointment? _____

_____

_____

_____

_____

_____

Can you ever recall bumping up against a glass ceiling, and realizing there was no more room for advancement at your workplace? What did you do about it? _____

_____

_____

_____

_____

Can you remember thinking that the career you really wanted was beyond your reach? Why did you think that? What did you do about it? _____

_____

_____

_____

_____

Can you think of a time when you realized you had more responsibility than you could handle? What did you do about it? _____

_____

_____

_____

_____

Can you think of a time when you felt like you were two different people at home and at work? How did you finally reconcile the two? _____

_____

_____

_____

_____

_____

Has your commitment to your career put strain on you or your family? What did you do about it? _____

_____

_____

_____

_____

_____

Have you ever lost your job? What was your response when you got the news? How did you get over the shock, and move on? _____

_____

_____

_____

_____

Have you ever invented a job for yourself or started your own business? Describe. _____

_____

_____

_____

_____

Q&A Topic #2: Breakthroughs

Creativity

Have you ever surprised yourself with how well you did on some creative undertaking? Describe. _____

_____

_____

_____

_____

_____

Have you ever solved a problem that other people said couldn't be solved? Explain. _____

_____

_____

_____

_____

_____

Did you ever have a good idea for an invention? Describe.

_____

_____

_____

_____

Can you think of a time when you were motivated to keep a journal or write a poem, play, or story? What brought it on? _____

_____

_____

_____

_____

Have you been in a play, opera, concert, musical, dance, or other performance as an adult? What was it like for you being onstage or behind the scenes? _____

_____

_____

_____

_____

_____

_____

_____

Have you ever taken a class or workshop that led you to discover a new creative outlet, or pursue it more seriously? Describe. _____

_____

_____

_____

_____

_____

_____

_____

Have you ever been inspired to capture a scene, mental image or idea on film, paper, or canvas? Describe. _____

_____

_____

_____

_____

_____

_____

_____

Relationships

Is there one relationship that has weathered more storms than others in your adult life? Describe. How did those troubles make the relationship evolve or grow stronger? __

_____

_____

_____

_____

_____

_____

_____

Have you been able to relate to your parent(s) and sibling(s)as an adult, without retreating to your childhood role with them? How did your relationship evolve? _____

_____

_____

_____

_____

_____

_____

_____

Have you ever called a friend in the wee hours of the morning to help you with a problem? Describe. _____

_____

_____

_____

_____

_____

_____

What aspect of the family life you've chosen turned out to be as rewarding as it was challenging? _____

_____

_____

_____

_____

_____

If you have children, can you think of a time as a parent you knew you'd faced a serious parenting test, and passed? __

_____

_____

_____

_____

_____

If you have a significant other, what was the turning point in your relationship when you determined you would try your damnedest to make it work? _____

_____

_____

_____

_____

_____

Can you think of a time when you realized you didn't need your relationships to define you as person? Describe. ____

_____

_____

_____

_____

Q&A Topic #3: Community
Workplace

Can you think of a company, work team, project or task force you felt particularly honored to belong to? Why? __

_____

_____

_____

_____

_____

Have you had work colleagues you felt you could rely on in case of a personal or family emergency? Who? Has this situation ever actually presented itself? What happened? __

_____

_____

_____

_____

What can you recall about your colleagues' lives outside of work? How did you learn this about them? _____

_____

_____

_____

_____

Have you had work colleagues become friends? How did you make that transition in your relationship? _____

_____

_____

_____

_____

Have you ever formed a business partnership? Describe. How do you feel about that partnership? _____

_____

_____

_____

_____

_____

How would you describe your career? _____

_____

_____

_____

_____

_____

_____

_____

_____

_____

_____

_____

_____

_____

_____

_____

_____

Spiritual

If you have a religious affiliation, can you remember when you made a commitment to your current community of faith, and why? _____

_____

_____

_____

_____

_____

Have you ever taken part in services outside of the religion you currently practice? How do you think it affected your thinking about religion? _____

_____

_____

_____

_____

Can you remember a time when you sought spiritual guidance to make an important and difficult life decision? __

_____

_____

_____

_____

Have you ever parted ways with other members of your religion over doctrinal matters? Describe. _____

_____

_____

_____

_____

Civic ties

When you walked down the street where you lived at the time, whom did you greet by name? How did you know these people? _____

_____

_____

_____

_____

Can you think of an instance when a neighbor came through for you or your family? What about a time when you came through for your neighbors? _____

_____

_____

_____

_____

Have you ever run for an official position in a civic group or city government? What position? Why? _____

_____

_____

_____

_____

Have you volunteered at a local school, non-profit organization, community group, or arts organization? Why? Can you recall hitting it off with someone you met while volunteering? Describe. _____

_____

_____

_____

Q&A Topic #4: Adventure

Travel

What's the farthest you've ever been from your home? What led you to that place? _____

_____

_____

_____

_____

_____

What do you always carry with you when you travel, and why? _____

_____

_____

_____

_____

_____

What's the worst trip you ever took? Why? _____

_____

_____

_____

_____

_____

What about the best trip you ever took? Why? _____

_____

_____

_____

_____

_____

What's the strangest place you ever spent the night? _____

_____

_____

_____

_____

_____

Have you ever gotten lost or in trouble in a strange place, and a complete stranger helped you? Did you ever pass on the favor to another complete stranger? Describe. _____

_____

_____

_____

_____

_____

What's the most bizarre food you've ever eaten? Why did you eat it? _____

_____

_____

_____

_____

_____

Have you kept in touch with someone you met while traveling? Who? Why? _____

_____

_____

_____

_____

_____

Personal risks

Have you ever risked life or limb to help someone else? Describe. _____

_____

_____

_____

_____

_____

_____

What professional risk have you taken that was especially brave? Explain. _____

_____

_____

_____

_____

_____

_____

Have you ever taken the leap and quit your job, started a family, or embarked on a new career when it wasn't the practical thing to do? Describe. What did you get out of that experience? _____

_____

_____

_____

_____

_____

How bold are you about inserting your opinion into a conversation that interests or concerns you? Can you give an example? _____

_____
_____
_____
_____
_____
_____
_____

Can you think of a time you entrusted someone with a deeply personal problem? What came of it? _____

_____
_____
_____
_____
_____
_____
_____

Have you ever sought forgiveness for something you've done? Can you think of a time you forgave someone who wronged you? Explain. _____

_____
_____
_____
_____
_____
_____
_____

The Artifacts Method

To bring your memories to the surface, try digging up a few artifacts of adulthood. Pick at least three items from the lists below to examine, and use the accompanying questions as a guide to further discoveries. If you pay close attention to these objects, you'll find they have a lot to say about the person you are.

Photos of friends and family taken as adults:

When were these photos taken? What was happening in your life at that time, and how is that reflected in this photo? _____

_____

_____

_____

Have any of your friends or relatives captured in a photograph died since the photo was taken? _____

_____

_____

_____

Which friends or relatives in these photos are you out of touch with? Why? _____

_____

_____

_____

Which friends or relatives in these photos are you still in touch with? Why? _____

_____

_____

Doctor's reports, lab results, and medicine vials:

Why did you need to take these medicines? Is this a medical condition you still have? _____

_____

_____

_____

_____

_____

Can you remember the doctor's visit when you were diagnosed with a medical condition? Were you scared? Relieved? Why? _____

_____

_____

_____

_____

Did any of those lab results keep you up nights worrying? Did you make any promises to yourself about what you would do if you were healthy? Explain. _____

_____

_____

_____

_____

Who was with you when you received your results? How did they help you come to terms with your diagnosis? __

_____

_____

_____

_____

Your own creations (sketches, stories, paintings, photos, sculpture, pottery, poetry, furniture, clothing, music, jewelry, gifts):

How much of your time went into making this? Why do you think you spent so much time on it? _____

_____

_____

_____

_____

_____

Did you make this with a particular person in mind? What did you like best about the process of making this piece?

_____

_____

_____

_____

_____

Did anyone help you in making this piece? Who? How?

_____

_____

_____

_____

Is there some aspect of this piece—a turn of phrase, a choice of color, a shape—that is a particular point of pride for you?

_____

_____

_____

_____

Cards, notes, e-mails and letters from friends, relations and neighbors (especially thank you notes, sympathy cards, congratulations, invitations, and apologies):

Can you recall what it meant to you to get this card or letter? Describe. _____

_____

_____

_____

_____

Do you suspect that any of these cards or letters might have been difficult for the sender to write? Which ones? Why?

_____

_____

_____

_____

Postcards or souvenirs:

What particularly impressed you about the places pictured on these postcards or souvenirs? _____

_____

_____

_____

_____

Does looking at this item bring back any tastes, smells or sounds from its place of origin? Describe. _____

_____

_____

_____

_____

Resume:

Do you recognize yourself from your resume? Why or why not? _____

_____

_____

_____

_____

_____

_____

_____

Which of your career accomplishments looks most impressive on paper? Did you actually like this job? Explain. __

_____

_____

_____

_____

_____

_____

What career blooper did you purposely leave out of your resume? _____

_____

_____

_____

_____

_____

_____

The Interviews Method

If you've hit upon a topic you'd like to explore further or aren't sure your memory serves you correctly, you might want to interview people who've known you well as an adult. Choose interview candidates from The Usual Suspects list below, or identify a few candidates of your own. Their accounts can help broaden your perspective and ground your story in fact. Be sure to ask your interview subjects in advance if they can spare an hour for the interview—that way they won't get testy halfway through, and you'll get much better material. The Sample Interview Questions included below should get your interview rolling.

The Usual Suspects

Parents
Siblings
Significant others
Children
Relatives
Neighbors
Fellow members of your religious community
Doctors
Volunteer coordinators
Fellow volunteers, civic group leaders, or committee members
Teachers
Fellow book club or discussion group members
Business partners
Bosses
Co-workers (current and former)
Friends (recent and longtime)
Support group members
Others: _____

Sample Interview Questions

Here are six interview questions to get you started—feel free to supplement or replace these questions with your own. You may want to record the interview on a voice recorder, and jot down the most interesting quotes here later on. Keep in mind that a single question can take 5-10 minutes to answer, depending on how chatty your interviewee is and whether you ask follow-up questions.

I remember that you were there when I _____.
What do you remember about that time? _____

_____

_____

_____

_____

_____

How would you have described me as an adult to someone who hadn't met me? _____

_____

_____

_____

_____

_____

What five words always seemed to crop up in our conversations back then? Why? _____

_____

_____

_____

_____

Can you tell me what one life experience I referred to most often as an adult? Why do you think that is? _____

_____

_____

_____

_____

_____

_____

_____

Could you tell me what political issue, religious concern or career crisis I've seemed most concerned about in my adult life? Why do you think that is? _____

_____

_____

_____

_____

_____

_____

_____

What is the one thing I've done as an adult that's most surprised you? Why? _____

_____

_____

_____

_____

_____

_____

_____

_____

_____

_____

_____

_____

_____

_____

_____

_____

_____

_____

_____

_____

_____

_____

_____

_____

_____

_____

_____

_____

_____

_____

_____

_____

_____

_____

_____

SELF-REALIZATION

Think back...

Congratulations! You've come into your own at last, and here's where your story really gets good. As Robert Browning once said: "The best is yet to be,/The last of life, for which the first is made." Now that you're no longer living each day in restless anticipation of the next, you can actually enjoy your journey.

So forget all that stuff you heard about whiling away the hours in a rocking chair. That's far too anticlimactic for a story as compelling as yours. You'll establish an inner circle, build a legacy, maybe even take a breather in a rocking chair now and again—but stay there? Perish the thought! Self-realization isn't about loitering around on the porch; it's about finding your feet, and using them.

You haven't come this far to lose momentum now. Let reflection and self-discovery continue to propel your life and your narrative ever onward. Even as you fill these pages with important relationships, consuming passions, and impressive accomplishments, leave yourself plenty of room to add more. After all, you're on the verge of becoming an accomplished autobiographer—there's no telling what you might do next.

Forge ahead!

Where to begin? Anywhere you want—personal convictions, enjoying the family you've made for yourself, ditching your book club for tango lessons. Basically, whenever you feel you started living life the way you really meant to live it all along. Write your life as vividly and truthfully as you live it, until you run out of space in this book. That's a sign you're ready to keep a journal—and maybe start on the next version of your autobiography.

Below are three methods to get your memories out of your subconscious, and onto paper where they belong. These are Q&A, Artifacts, and Interviews. Try one method that comes naturally, and one that challenges you—it'll enrich your autobiography, and your experience of writing it too.

The Q&A Method

*Jot down your responses to at least a few of the questions that seem relevant to you under each of the four main topics: **Inner Circle, Legacy, Reflection and Discovery**. Feel free to add others or go off on tangents as the spirit moves you. If you find yourself hesitating, you might try reading the questions aloud and recording your spoken answers with a voice recorder. Then as you play back your recording, write down the interesting parts of your answers and elaborate on them as you see fit. Your answers should bring your life experience into focus, and provide a few juicy anecdotes besides.*

Q&A Topic #1: Inner circle

Family

What family relationships have proved to be the most important to you? Why? _____

_____

_____

_____

_____

_____

If you have a life partner, what was it about this person that led you to conclude that this was the one for you? What makes you a good match for one another? _____

_____

_____

_____

_____

_____

Have you had a spouse or life partner die? How did you deal with it? _____

_____

_____

_____

_____

_____

Do you have children, grandchildren, or great-grandchildren? What are their names? _____

_____

_____

_____

_____

_____

What five words spring to mind to describe each of them?

_____

_____

_____

_____

_____

If you were to brag about your kids or grandchildren, what would you say about each of them? _____

_____

_____

_____

_____

_____

If you were to confess your hopes for each of your grand-children, what would they be? _____

_____

_____

_____

_____

_____

Do any of your grandchildren remind you of your children when they were young? How? _____

_____

_____

_____

_____

_____

Where do your grandchildren live? What role do you play in their lives? _____

_____

_____

_____

_____

_____

If you have siblings, what is your relationship like to each of them today? What would you say has been the defining moment in your relationship as adults? _____

_____

_____

_____

_____

_____

Are you an aunt or an uncle? What do you most appreciate about your niece or nephew? _____

_____

_____

_____

_____

_____

Are you especially close to any of your extended relations? Whom? How did you get to be so close? _____

_____

_____

_____

_____

_____

Is there anyone in your life who you consider an adopted family member? How did you get so close? _____

_____

_____

_____

_____

Friends

What friendships have proved to be the most important to you? Why? _____

_____
_____
_____
_____
_____

Who are your closest friends? Do you have friends that you've known for years and years? What phases have you seen one another through? _____

_____
_____
_____
_____
_____

Which friends do you call first when you receive good news? Which friends are there for you in difficult situations? _____

_____
_____
_____
_____

Has a close friend passed away? How did you deal with it?

_____
_____
_____
_____

Have you found new friends later on in life, even when you felt like you had enough already? Who were they? How did you meet? _____

_____

_____

_____

_____

_____

If you still keep in touch with people from your former workplace(s), how did your relationship come to be so close?

_____

_____

_____

_____

_____

Which neighbors do you appreciate most? Why? _____

_____

_____

_____

_____

Do you have neighbors who check in on you when you're sick, keep an eye on your home or take care of your pet when you're out of town? How did you build this level of trust with one another? _____

_____

_____

_____

_____

Career achievements

What would you say are the highlights of your career?
Why? _____

_____

_____

_____

_____

_____

What would you say was the toughest job you ever had?
Describe. How did you handle it? _____

_____

_____

_____

_____

_____

How many different careers would you say you've had by
this point in your life? Name each of them. _____

_____

_____

_____

_____

Can you think of any people you mentored in the course of
your career? What have these people gone on to achieve?

_____

_____

_____

_____

What lines of work did you become proficient enough at doing that you felt confident you could always fall back on them if you wanted to? _____

_____

_____

_____

_____

_____

What's the most satisfying job you've ever had? Why? __

_____

_____

_____

_____

_____

Have you ever carved out a niche for yourself or otherwise made yourself indispensible in your workplace? _____

_____

_____

_____

_____

_____

What job taught you the most about yourself as a person? How so? _____

_____

_____

_____

_____

_____

Commitments

What community groups that you've joined over the years have been the most meaningful to you? Why? _____

_____

_____

_____

_____

_____

In what ways do you think you've been a good role model for the younger people in your family or community? ____

_____

_____

_____

_____

What makes you most proud of your family? How would you say you've contributed to that aspect of your family life?

_____

_____

_____

_____

How have you manifested your spiritual convictions in your life? _____

_____

_____

_____

In what ways do you consider yourself an active citizen? How has this changed over the years? _____

_____

_____

_____

_____

_____

Have you committed substantial time or money to a particular cause? Which one(s), and why? _____

_____

_____

_____

_____

_____

Can you think of a time when you've been moved to take action by some distressing news? Describe. _____

_____

_____

_____

_____

_____

In what ways do you think of yourself as an active global citizen? _____

_____

_____

_____

_____

_____

Recognition

Have you received any awards, acclaim, or peer recognition for your efforts? Describe. Can you recall the moment when you first heard you'd been singled out for recognition? ___

_____

_____

_____

_____

Has a party or special gathering ever been held in your honor? What was the occasion, and why do you think the attendees wanted to celebrate you? _____

_____

_____

_____

_____

Has something you made ever appeared in an art show or exhibition? Describe. How did it feel to see your work on display? _____

_____

_____

_____

_____

Have you ever been invited to give a speech or toast, or read something you wrote at a special occasion? Describe. ____

_____

_____

_____

Have you ever been quoted in an article or book, or had your ideas published or referred to in print? Describe. Can you recall how it felt when you first saw your name in print?

_____

_____

_____

_____

_____

Have you ever found your photo displayed in the home of a friend or loved one? How did you feel the first time you noticed it? _____

_____

_____

_____

_____

_____

Have you been consulted or referred to as an expert in your field? Describe. _____

_____

_____

_____

_____

Have you ever received a personal letter of thanks or admiration from someone you helped or inspired? Describe. __

_____

_____

_____

_____

Self-definition

If asked to describe yourself, what five words immediately spring to mind? Why? How is this different from how you've defined yourself earlier in life? _____

_____

_____

_____

_____

What would you say have been the defining moments in your life? Why? _____

_____

_____

_____

_____

Do you feel yourself to be a religious or spiritual person? Why or why not? _____

_____

_____

_____

_____

If you are religious, which elements of your religious practice or beliefs seemed to come most naturally to you, and which ones have been the most challenging for you? Why?

_____

_____

_____

_____

Can you recall an experience that was difficult for you, but has proved to be a wellspring of personal growth? Describe.

_____
_____
_____
_____
_____
_____
_____

Have you ever gone through a time of serious reflection or soul-searching? What brought it on? What did you find out about yourself? _____

_____
_____
_____
_____
_____
_____

Have you ever been a teacher, or shared your knowledge with others? What did you learn about yourself from the experience of teaching others? _____

_____
_____
_____
_____
_____
_____
_____

What would you most like your epitaph to say about you?

_____

_____

_____

_____

_____

How would you like to be remembered? _____

_____

_____

_____

_____

_____

_____

_____

_____

_____

_____

_____

_____

_____

_____

_____

_____

_____

Making your peace

Is there a person or a group of people that has helped you come to terms with parts of your life that have long troubled you? How so? _____

_____
_____
_____
_____
_____
_____
_____

Can you think of a time when you've gone back and asked forgiveness or made amends for a mistake you've made? __

_____
_____
_____
_____
_____
_____
_____

Have you ever personally thanked someone for making a difference in your life or the lives of your loved ones? Describe. _____

_____
_____
_____
_____
_____
_____

Q&A Topic #4: Discovery

Continuing revelations

What subjects are you just beginning to learn about that recently captured your imagination? Can you think of a time recently that you took a class on a whim, and got really involved in it? How so? _____

_____

_____

_____

_____

What have been your most satisfying creative outlets as a mature adult? Explain. _____

_____

_____

_____

_____

Have you joined a book club or discussion group as an adult? Describe. _____

_____

_____

_____

Which friends or relatives get you thinking and talking about subjects you never would've imagined would interest you? Can you give an example of this? _____

_____

_____

_____

Can you think of an activity you've taken up that you never would've imagined yourself enjoying before? How did you get started? _____

_____

_____

_____

_____

_____

_____

Can you think of a lecture, play, art show or performance you attended as an adult that had an especially strong impact on you? Why? _____

_____

_____

_____

_____

_____

_____

Can you think of a recent book, album, or movie that got you thinking and kept you thinking for a long time? What was it? _____

_____

_____

_____

_____

_____

Plans

Now that you've reflected on your life thus far, how would you like to change it in the years ahead? _____

_____

_____

_____

_____

_____

What are the three places you'd most like to visit in your lifetime? Why? _____

_____

_____

_____

_____

_____

What are the top three places you'd like to return to, and spend some more time? _____

_____

_____

_____

_____

_____

Who would you most like to spend more time with in the coming years? Why? _____

_____

_____

_____

_____

Are there any old friends you'd particularly like to get in touch with again? Who? Why? _____

_____

_____

_____

_____

_____

_____

_____

What one change would you most like to see in the world in your lifetime, and how do you think you might go about making it happen? _____

_____

_____

_____

_____

_____

_____

If you could make one wish for yourself in the coming year, what would it be? How might you make that wish come true? _____

_____

_____

_____

_____

_____

_____

_____

Now that you've written your autobiography, what's next?

_____

_____

_____

_____

_____

_____

_____

_____

_____

_____

_____

_____

_____

_____

_____

_____

_____

_____

_____

_____

_____

_____

_____

_____

_____

The Artifacts Method

To bring your memories to the surface, try digging up a few souvenirs. Pick at least three items from the list below to examine, and use the accompanying questions as a guide to further discoveries. If you pay close attention to these objects, you'll find they have a lot to say about the person you are.

Photos of friends and family

Which of these photos enjoy prime placement in your home or workplace? Why? _____

_____

_____

_____

_____

_____

Which photos are tattered because you've carried them around everywhere? _____

_____

_____

_____

_____

_____

When you look at a photo you took of your family, do you notice an expression on a family member's face that only you could capture or recognize? Describe. _____

_____

_____

_____

_____

Find the oldest photos of you with your closest friends. What are you doing in them? _____

_____

_____

_____

_____

_____

_____

_____

_____

Do you have photos of yourself with your friends at major events in your life? What can you remember your friends saying or doing at these events? _____

_____

_____

_____

_____

_____

_____

_____

Do you keep photos of loved ones that are no longer with us? Describe. _____

_____

_____

_____

_____

_____

_____

_____

Cards, notes, e-mails and letters from loved ones, relations, and neighbors (especially love letters, personal notes, birth or wedding announcements, and other special occasion cards):

Are there parts of any of these cards or letters that you know by heart? Which ones? Why do you remember them so clearly? _____

_____

_____

_____

_____

Which of these cards and letters can you remember being thrilled to receive? Why? _____

_____

_____

_____

Were any of these written by a relative of yours as a child? Describe the card or letter. What does it remind you about that person as a child? _____

_____

_____

_____

Did any of these say something you especially needed to hear at the time? What? Why was that message so welcome? _____

_____

_____

_____

Recognition from community organizations where you've contributed time or money (certificates, thank-you letters, plaques, gifts, etc.):

What did you have to give up to make this commitment of time or money? _____

_____

_____

_____

_____

_____

What did your efforts and funding help to accomplish? __

_____

_____

_____

_____

_____

Who was the person who thanked you for your contributions? _____

_____

_____

_____

_____

_____

Do you remember receiving this recognition? Describe. __

_____

_____

_____

_____

Your autobiography:

When you first started this autobiography, did you ever really think you'd make it this far? What motivated you to begin anyway? What encouraged you to stick with it? __

_____

_____

_____

_____

_____

_____

_____

Did the act of writing this autobiography bring you to any unexpected realizations? Describe. _____

_____

_____

_____

_____

_____

_____

_____

Looking back on your life as captured in this autobiography, are there certain themes that emerge? What are they? __

_____

_____

_____

_____

_____

_____

_____

The Interviews Method

If you've hit upon a topic you'd like to explore further or aren't sure your memory serves you correctly, you might want to interview people who've known you well in recent years. Choose interview candidates from The Usual Suspects list below, or identify a few candidates of your own. Their accounts can help broaden your perspective and ground your story in fact. Be sure to ask your interview subjects in advance if they can spare an hour for the interview—that way they won't get testy halfway through, and you'll get much better material. The Sample Interview Questions included below should get your interview rolling.

The Usual Suspects

Parents
Siblings
Friends (recent and longtime)
Significant others
Children
Grandchildren
Other relatives
Close neighbors
Volunteer coordinators
Fellow volunteers or civic leaders
Students
Teachers
Fellow book club or discussion group members
Fellow members of your religious community
Former colleagues
Support group members
Others: _____

Sample Interview Questions

Here are six interview questions to get you started—feel free to supplement or replace these questions with your own. You may want to record the interview on a voice recorder, and jot down the most interesting quotes here later on. Keep in mind that a single question can take 5-10 minutes to answer, depending on how chatty your interviewee is and whether you ask follow-up questions.

I remember that you were there when I _____.
What do you remember about that time?   _____

_____
_____
_____
_____
_____

What's your all-time favorite anecdote about me, and why?

_____
_____
_____
_____
_____
_____

What five names always seem to crop up in our conversations? Why do you think this is?   _____

_____
_____
_____
_____

What would you say are my three most lasting contributions to the world? Why? _____

_____
_____
_____
_____
_____
_____
_____

Could you tell me what social issue, family or personal concern I've seemed most concerned about in life? _____

_____
_____
_____
_____
_____
_____
_____

What would be your top three predictions for me in the years ahead? _____

_____
_____
_____
_____
_____
_____

_____

_____

_____

_____

_____

_____

_____

_____

_____

_____

_____

_____

_____

_____

_____

_____

_____

_____

_____

_____

_____

_____

_____

_____

_____

_____

_____

_____

_____

_____

_____